Why not make your own family tree —
you can draw pictures of your family or use photographs!

JACK COTTON (Grandpa)
Bookseller

married

MERRY COTTON (Grandma)
Bookseller

AUNT MARIGOLD
(Poppy's great-aunt)

JAMES COTTON
(Dad)
Landscape Gardener

SAFFLOWER THIMBLE
(Poppy's aunt)
Potter

married

SORRELL THIMBLE
(Poppy's uncle)
Artist

PRINCESS POPPY COTTON

SAFFRON SAGE
(Poppy's cousin)
Fashion designer

married

DAVID SAGE
Vet

Princess Poppy's A – Z of favourite people, places and things!

Four of Poppy's favourite things are missing – can you find the right stickers to complete her A – Z?

A – Aunt Marigold's General Store

B – Beehive Beauty Salon

C – Cornsilk Castle

D – Daisy

E – Edward

F – Forget-Me-Not Cottage – Grandpa lives here

G – Grandpa

H – Honey – My best friend

I – Ice-cream – My favourite is strawberry!

J – Jewellery Box

K – Kitchen time – I love baking with Mum

L – Lavender Lake School of Dance

Why not make your own A – Z of favourite people, places and things – stick it into your yearbook, just like I do!

M – Mimosa – she lives at the Hedgerows Hotel

N – Necklace – I love my sparkly birthday necklace

O – Out and about

P – Princess Poppy – this is me!

Q – Quay – Paddle Steamer Quay

R – Ruby – My favourite doll

S – Saffron

T – Twinkletoes – mine and Honey's pony

U – Umbrella – my favourite one has polka dots

V – Vet's Surgery – Uncle David works here

W – Wedding dress – Me in Saffron's wedding dress!

X – as in box – my dress came in a beautiful box

Y – Yearbook – I stick photos and special things in here

Z – Zoo – Mum and Dad have promised to take me soon

Draw a Picture of Princess Poppy

Use the Princess Poppy picture to help you complete your drawing
and then add the tiara sticker to finish it off!

Draw a Picture of Honey

Use the Honey picture to help you complete your drawing
and then add the fairy wand sticker to finish it off!

Window Dressing

Saffron changes the window display at her shop every week –
this week the theme is weddings. There are still some things missing –
can you find the right stickers to help Saffron complete her window display?

The Great Honeypot Hill Treasure Hunt

It's the Great Honeypot Hill Treasure Hunt today –
can you help Poppy find all the things on her list?
The first person to find everything wins
a cream tea at Bumble Bee's Teashop!

N
W ✦ E
S

Saffron Thimble's
Sewing Shop

The Orchards

Paddle Steamer
Quay

Aunt
Marigold's
General
Store

Healing House and Garden

Lavender Valley
Garden Centre

The Worthingtons' House

Melody
Maker's
Music Shop

Lavender Lake

Bumble Bee's Teashop

Lavender Lake
School of Dance

Rosehip
School

SCHOOL

Hedgerows Hotel
Where Mimosa lives

Summer
Meadow

Wildspice Woods

Just circle each item on the picture when you find it and tick it off my list.

A bridge ☐   A fountain ☐

A Cat ☐   A cow ☐

A dog ☐   A horse ☐

A tractor ☐   A sheep ☐

Honeysuckle Cottage
Poppy's House

Forget-Me-Not Cottage
Grandpa's House and Office

Poppy Field

Cornsilk Castle
and Courtyard

Honeypot Cottage
ney and Granny Bumble's House

Blossom
Bakehouse

Village Hall

Office

Sage's
Vet Surgery

Beehive
Beauty Salon

River Swan

Barley Farm
The Meadowsweets' House

Honeypot Hill
Railway Station

Shopping at Aunt Marigold's General Store

The cupboard is bare and mum is very busy with the twins so she has given Poppy a shopping list and asked her to go to Aunt Marigold's General Store to pick up some food. Find the right stickers to make Mum's shopping list complete.

SHOPPING LIST

10 shiny

A bag of

1 slab of smelly

1 bottle of Aunt Marigold's

2 loaves of fresh crusty

1 jar of yummy

Some tasty

See whether you can find all the things on Poppy's list in the picture below.

Spot the Difference

These two pictures of Mum and Poppy in the playroom appear
to be the same, but if you look really carefully you will see
that there are 10 differences. Can you find them all?

When you find them, circle the changes on the picture below.

Princess Poppy's Photo Album

Princess Poppy is sticking all her favourite photos into an album, but some of them are missing. Use the stickers to help Poppy complete her album.

Working on
Holly Mallow's stall

Me and Honey at the Fair Day Ball

My play in the garden

Me in my
special birthday dress

Wrapped up for the winter!

Ruby,
my favourite doll

Me and honey starring in Coppé...

Me with Mum and Dad

Don't we
look gorgeous!

Best friends for ever!

Why not make your own album with some of your favourite photographs!

Colouring by Numbers!

Poppy was a perfect princess on her birthday.
Find the painting pallette sticker, then follow the numbers to
brighten up Poppy's party. Use coloured pencils or felt tips.
Choose any colour you like for the flowers.

Princess Poppy's Wardrobe

Princess Poppy's things are all over the place – can you help her
to get everything organized by working out where each item lives?
Draw an arrow to the correct section of Poppy's wardrobe
and everything will be spick and span in no time!

coat hook

cardigans

hanging space
for dresses

hooks for bags
and umbrellas

hats

t-shirts

winter
jumpers

craft
clothes

socks

tights

boots

shorts

shoes

trousers

Baking with Princess Poppy and Honey

Poppy and Honey are making Rocky Road Cakes together, but need some help tracking down all the ingredients. Here's a list of what they need – use the stickers to help Poppy and Honey find everything, and then make your very own cakes from their brilliant recipe.

Ingredients

❖ 4oz butter

❖ 1 tablespoon golden syrup

❖ 2 dessert spoons drinking chocolate

❖ 1/2 lb of crushed digestive biscuits – crush in a bag with a rolling pin.

❖ 1/2 drop of vanilla essence

❖ big bar of cooking chocolate for melting over the mixture

goodies: handful of sultanas, cherries, marshmallows or Malteasers – you choose!

Turn over to find out how to make a Rocky Road Cake exactly like mine and Poppy's — don't forget to ask a grown-up for help!

Rocky Road Cakes Recipe

Utensils

- ❖ swiss roll tin
- ❖ 2 saucepans
- ❖ wooden spoons
- ❖ weighing scales
- ❖ heatproof dish for melting chocolate
- ❖ rolling pin

What to do now

1. Ask a grown-up to melt the butter in a pan, then add the sugar and golden syrup. Add the drinking chocolate, crushed digestive biscuits and vanilla essence

2. Then add the 'goodies' of your choice

3. Press the mixture into the swiss roll tin and put in the fridge to chill

4. While the cake is chilling, break the bar of cooking chocolate into smallish pieces and put into a heatproof bowl. Ask a grown-up to put this over a pan of boiling water and leave until chocolate is melted

5. Take the cake out of the fridge, spread the melted chocolate over it and put back in the fridge until the chocolate is set

6. When the chocolate has set, take the cake out of the fridge and ask a grown-up to help you cut it into squares, rectangles or triangles.

Find the right sticker to complete our tea —
and see what the Rocky Road Cakes look like!

On Barley Farm
A Sticker Storybook

Hi there!
In this brilliant sticker storybook some
of the pictures have bits missing. Use the
75 colour stickers in the middle of the
book to help you complete each scene.
Have fun!

Written by Janey Louise Jones

PICTURE CORGI

Poppy often helped Farmer Meadowsweet
and his wife on Barley Farm.

In summer, she picked strawberries and made jam.

In autumn, she helped with the harvest.

In winter, she fed the animals with Farmer Meadowsweet.

But spring is Poppy's favourite time on the farm
because that's when all the baby animals are born.

One spring morning Poppy arrived at the farm to discover that some new lambs had been born during the night – the first lambs of the year! She couldn't wait to see them.

Lambs are Poppy's favourite baby animals because they're so cute and cuddly!

"There's one little lamb in particular that I think you should meet," said Farmer Meadowsweet.

"Follow me . . ."

Poppy peeped inside the pen, and there, among all the
fluffy white lambs was a beautiful black lamb with
huge brown eyes that were looking up at Poppy.

"We've called him Sooty," explained Farmer Meadowsweet.
"He's already a right bundle of mischief and he's not even
a day old yet!"

"Aw, he's perfect!" exclaimed Poppy. "Can I cuddle him?"

"Of course you can, but I'll tell you now, he's not the cuddly sort, he's an explorer!" said the farmer.

Poppy climbed into the pen and very slowly and gently reached down to stroke the little black lamb.

"I think he likes you," smiled Farmer Meadowsweet.
"Would you like to help me look after him?"
    "Yes, please," smiled Poppy.

"Well," replied Farmer Meadowsweet, "his mother doesn't have quite enough milk to feed all her babies and Sooty is a greedy little thing, so we're going to bottle-feed him up at the farmhouse. Come with me, I'll show you how."

Every day Poppy fed Sooty in the big cosy farmhouse kitchen.

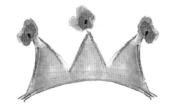

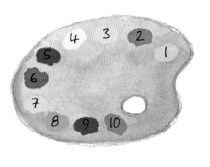

GOLDEN SYRUP

BUTTER

drinking chocolate

caster sugar

CHOCOLATE

digestive biscuits

1

3

5

6

7

2

4

8

9

10

11

12

13

14

15

16

17

18

19

21

23

20

22

33

24

25

26

32

31

27

28

29

35

34

30

36

3

39

40

41

45

46

44

48

42

43

47

I

49

50

52

53

68

69

55

56

70

71

57

59

72

73

63

62

66

74

75

65

67

She absolutely adored him and she loved going down to the farm each morning.

But one morning, she arrived to find the farm in total chaos –
Sooty had escaped!

"Don't worry, Farmer Meadowsweet, I'll find him," said Poppy, sounding much more confident than she felt.

Poor Poppy was actually frantic with worry. What if she never saw Sooty again?

"Hmm," thought Poppy, "maybe he's gone to play with some of the other baby animals."

First she checked the cow shed . . .

but there was no sign of him there. All she found was Freesia the
big black and white cow along with her beautiful little calf.

Next she looked in the pig pen . . .

it was feeding time for the six chubby piglets
but Sooty was nowhere to be seen.

Then Poppy decided to look for him in the stables . . .

but all she found was Fern, the bay mare,
with Harry, her little brown foal.

After that Poppy tried the chicken coop . . .

but there were so many new chicks,
there was hardly even room for the cockerel!

"Oh, dear!" Poppy said to herself. "Sooty hasn't even had his milk today – he'll be so hungry. Where *can* he be?"

60

61

62

63

Just then, Poppy had an idea . . .

She dashed back to the farmhouse and there, curled up with the sheepdog puppies in front of the hearth in the kitchen, was little Sooty looking very contented indeed.

"You naughty, little lamb," smiled Poppy, as she gave Sooty his milk at long last. "Don't you ever hide from me again, I was so worried."

Can you match all the baby farm animals to their mummies?
The stickers will help.

Sheep   Lambs   **Duck**   Ducklings

Pig   Piglets   **Chicken**   Chicks

Cat   Kittens   **Mare**   Foal

Sheepdog   Puppies   **Cow**   Calf

Petals and Picnics

A Make-and-Do Book

Written by Janey Louise Jones

PICTURE CORGI

Make a Princess Poppy Tiara

You will need

❖ A grown-up to help

❖ A tape measure

❖ A long piece of card – long enough to fit around your head plus 2 cm. Gold or silver card looks really special

❖ Scissors, glue and a stapler or sticky tape

❖ Glitter glue, stickers, coloured pens or pencils to decorate your tiara

❖ Small squares of coloured tissue paper

I know being a princess is on the inside, but I do so love wearing pretty princess things, especially tiaras!

1 Ask a grown-up to cut a long piece of card to the correct length

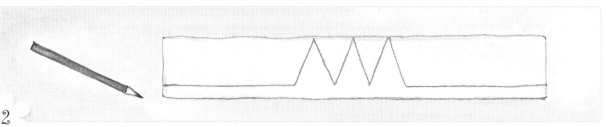

2 Draw a tiara shape onto the long piece of card, as shown

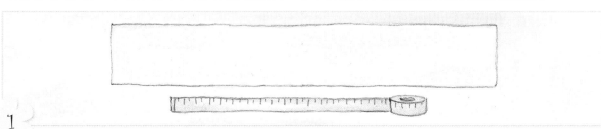

3 Ask a grown-up to help you cut it out

4
Now decorate your tiara with glitter glue, stickers, pens or pencils – or even all of these things!

5
Make flowers from the tissue paper – pinch the middle point of the squares and gather in folds, as shown. They will look just like flower heads!

6
Stick the flower heads onto each of the points and you'll have a tiara just like Poppy's

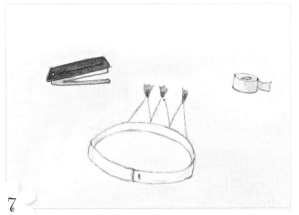

7
Leave everything to dry for 20–30 minutes, then ask a grown-up to clip the ends of the tiara together with sticky tape or a stapler. Make sure your tiara fits your head first!

We're perfect princesses now!

Make a Princess Poppy
Jewellery Box

You will need

❖ A grown-up to help

❖ Gold paint and a paint brush

❖ Scissors and glue

❖ An empty chocolate box – the bigger the better and it must have an insert tray

❖ Some fabric – enough to line the inside of the box. Red velvet looks super gorgeous, but you can use any fabric scraps you have around the house

❖ Stickers, sequins, beads, glitter glue or stick-on jewels

For my birthday my mum and dad gave me this really sparkly necklace and I want to keep it safe along with all my other precious things, so Mum showed me how to make a jewellery box.

1 Paint the empty chocolate box with shimmering gold paint. Leave to dry for 20–30 minutes

2 When the paint is dry, ask a grown-up to help you line the inside of the box by gluing the fabric and sticking it in place

3

Lay the insert tray inside the box — this will help you keep your jewellery tidy!

4

Decorate the outside of your box with stickers, sequins, glitter glue, beads or stick-on jewels

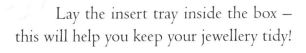

I'm going to put my jewellery box on my dressing table and I might even make one to give to Honey for her birthday!

Make a Melon Seed Necklace

You will need

- A grown-up to help
- A sieve
- The seeds from one melon
- A roll of kitchen paper
- A large needle and nylon thread
- Acrylic paints and a paint brush

My teacher, Holly Mallow, makes jewellery in her spare time. This pretty necklace is made from melon seeds and it's really simple to make!

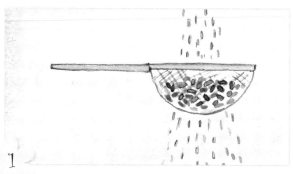

1   Ask a grown-up to cut open a melon. Spoon the seeds out and wash them in a sieve

2   Lay them out on kitchen paper and leave them somewhere warm to dry out for 2–3 hours – the airing cupboard is a good place

3   Once dry, you can paint the seeds any colour you like with watered down acrylic paints, and leave them to dry again, or leave the seeds their natural colour – they still look very pretty

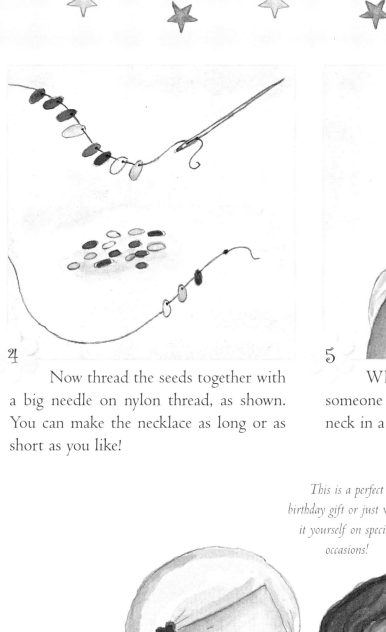

4 Now thread the seeds together with a big needle on nylon thread, as shown. You can make the necklace as long or as short as you like!

5 When you have finished, ask someone to tie the necklace around your neck in a secure knot

This is a perfect birthday gift or just wear it yourself on special occasions!

Make Friendship Bracelets with Poppy and Honey

You will need

❖ A grown-up to help

❖ Long, strong, thick thread in all your favourite colours – about 18cm long

❖ 1 piece of paper

❖ Sticky tape

Me and Honey have been best friends for ever so one day we decided to make friendship bracelets for each other. You can make them for your best friend too – it's easy!

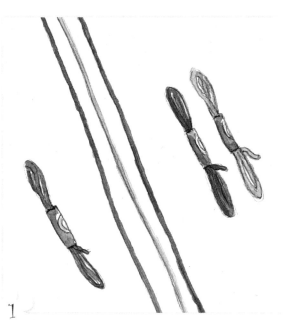

1

Choose three strands of different coloured thread – make sure they look nice together

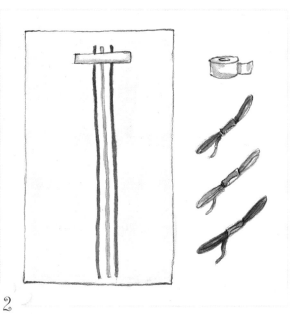

2

Stick one end of each thread onto the paper, as shown

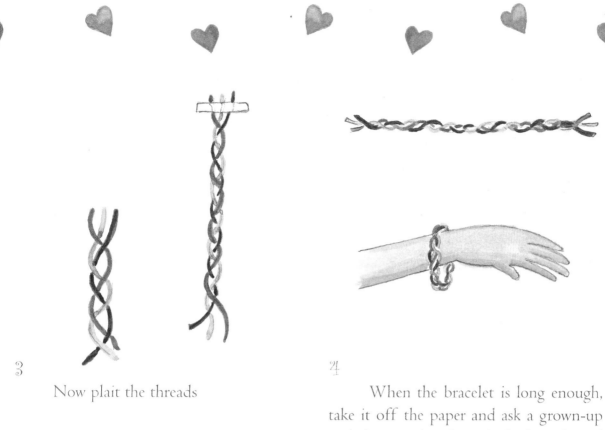

3

Now plait the threads

4

When the bracelet is long enough, take it off the paper and ask a grown-up to help you tie a knot in both ends and then fasten it around your wrist

Me and Honey have matching friendship bracelets to show that we're the best of friends!

Paint Pretty Shells and Pebbles

You will need

❖ A grown-up to help

❖ Acrylic paints and paint brushes

❖ Clear varnish and a brush or clear nail varnish

❖ Pebbles or shells

One day I went to the beach at Camomile Cove with Daisy. We collected lots of pretty pebbles and shells in our bucket and then went back to Daisy's house to decorate them. It was great fun, you should try it — you can find pebbles in lots of places, including the park or your garden!

I chose a smooth, pale pebble:

Daisy chose a shell:

1

First I painted it bright red

1

First she painted it all red

2

When the red paint was dry I painted a line to show the wings, dots and a black head

VARNISH

3

I waited for the black paint to dry too and then painted on eyes and a mouth in yellow, and when that was dry I varnished the whole pebble

I turned my pebble into a LADYBIRD and gave it to Grandpa to use as a paperweight. Daisy turned her shell into a STRAWBERRY and gave it to her mum as an ornament for her dressing table.

2

When the red paint was dry, Daisy painted a green husk and little green dots all over the shell

VARNISH

3

When the green paint was dry, Daisy varnished her shell

You can turn pebbles and shells into all sorts of different things by painting them.

Make an Easy Lavender Bag

You will need

❖ A grown-up to help

❖ A roll of kitchen paper

❖ Dried or fresh lavender –
1 handful for each lavender bag

❖ A square piece of muslin or
gauze 30x30cm

❖ 1 rubber band for each lavender bag

❖ 30cm of pretty ribbon (per bag) –
purple would look gorgeous

*Last week
Granny Bumble
took me to the Lavender
Lake Garden Centre. We
bought some lavender
and later on she showed
me how to make
lavender bags.*

1

Ask a grown-up to help you cut some lavender if you have it in your garden, if not, just buy some

2

Rub off the flower heads onto kitchen paper and if fresh lavender, leave to dry out somewhere warm for about a week

3

Ask a grown-up to help you cut out a square of muslin or gauze

4

Place the dried lavender on the middle of the square

5

Carefully gather up the edges – try not to spill any lavender! Fasten at the top with a rubber band, as shown

6

Tie the ribbon around the band, making sure you cover the band completely

Hang lavender bags around the house or put them in your wardrobe to make your clothes smell really gorgeous! They are lovely, sweet-smelling presents – perfect for Mother's Day!

Flower Pressing
with Princess Poppy

You will need

❖ A grown-up to help – Grandpas are good for this!

❖ A selection of your favourite flowers – Poppy's favourites are pansies, roses, tulips, daisies and poppies of course

❖ A roll of kitchen paper

❖ A flower press or some big heavy books – try a dictionary or an encyclopaedia

❖ Card, sticky-back plastic, glue and gold or silver pens

I want my favourite flowers to live for ever, so Grandpa showed me a way to do this. Every year we press lots of flowers and make cards and pictures out of them – it's easy and fun!

1
    Pick some flowers – always ask a grown-up first. Do not pick them after it has rained, as they must be dry

2
    Open the book near the back, lay some kitchen paper on the page, then put the flowers you want to press on the kitchen paper

3
Put another layer of kitchen paper on top of the flowers. Close the book

4
Add a few more heavy books on top to make sure the flowers press flat. Leave for between 1 and 3 weeks

5
When the flowers are pressed you can make cards or pictures with them. Stick the flowers onto card, cover with sticky-back plastic for a shiny finish and use as a Birthday or Christmas card, or put it in a picture frame and hang it on your wall!

My pressed-flower picture will look really pretty on my bedroom wall!

Make a Petal Princess
Pin Cushion

You will need

- ❖ A grown-up to help
- ❖ Scissors
- ❖ 2 squares of velvet, 16x16cm these will be called A1 and A2
- ❖ Another square of velvet, 16x16cm in a different colour to pieces A1 and A2. (This is called piece B)
- ❖ Gold thread and a needle
- ❖ Pins
- ❖ Stuffing (cotton wool works well)

Cousin Saffron has a really beautiful petal pin cushion that she made herself, and she helped me make one just like it!

1

For the petal shapes, fold piece B into 4, pin together and draw a petal shape as shown, then ask an adult to cut it out. You will end up with 4 petals, all the same size

2

Take piece A1, and pin the 4 petal-shaped pieces onto the velvety side in a flower pattern, as shown. Stitch on with gold thread as neatly as you can

3

Pin pieces A1 and A2 together as shown with the velvety bits touching, (right sides together)

4

Stitch around the edge. Don't forget to leave a space to turn it the right way round again!

5

Turn the right way round and fill your pin cushion as full as you can with stuffing

6

Now sew up the gap. Fold the edges in, as shown, pin together, then stitch as neatly as you can

Now you have a Petal Princess Pin Cushion to keep all your pins safe!

Have a Princess Poppy Picnic

I love picnics when the weather is nice and Aunt Marigold organizes the best ones ever — she says it's all in the planning!

What to take

- ❖ A cosy rug
- ❖ A table cloth
- ❖ Paper plates, plastic cups, napkins and straws
- ❖ Bats, balls, fishing nets
- ❖ Towels
- ❖ An umbrella and waterproofs just in case!

Food

Pack all your favourite foods — these are some of mine

- ❖ Cucumber sandwiches
- ❖ Aunt Marigold's home-made lemonade
- ❖ Iced cupcakes
- ❖ Apples, grapes, strawberries and raspberries

What to wear

- ❖ Shorts and t-shirt or a sundress — don't forget to bring a warm jumper or cardie
- ❖ Sun hat and sunglasses
- ❖ Sandals
- ❖ Swimming costume — put it on under your clothes

Here are a few tips for you so that you can have your very own Princess Poppy Picnic. Turn over for my favourite picnic recipes!

Aunt Marigold's cloudy lemonade

You will need

❖ 6 fresh lemons ❖ 6 tablespoons caster sugar ❖ Water to taste ($1\frac{1}{2}$ – 3 litres)

What to do

1. Ask a grown-up to boil the sugar and water – leave syrup to cool
2. Juice the lemons
3. Mix the lemon juice and the sugar/water syrup together
4. Dilute with water until it tastes just right

Poppy's favourite cucumber sandwiches

You will need

❖ Sliced bread – white or brown, whichever you like best ❖ Butter ❖ Cucumber

What to do

1. Butter the bread
2. Ask a grown-up to skin the cucumber and cut it into thin slices
3. Lay the sliced cucumber on the bread, slightly away from the crusts then put the top piece of bread on, butter-side down
4. Ask a grown-up to cut off the crusts and cut the sandwiches into dainty triangles

Cupcakes fit for a princess

You will need

❖ Plain cupcakes – homemade or bought ❖ 2 tablespoons icing sugar
❖ 1 teaspoon water ❖ Hundreds-and-thousands

What to do

1. Mix the icing sugar and water together
2. Spread mixture on top of the cakes
3. Sprinkle Hundreds-and-thousands on top and leave to set

Dressing up and Designing
with Princess Poppy

*Me and my
best friend Honey get
invited to lots of special parties
and play-times in Honeypot Hill
and we get dressed up for all of them.
We just love clothes! Turn over to
find out how to design us
some new clothes!*

Designing new clothes
for Poppy and Honey

You will need

❖ A grown-up to help

❖ Scissors, glue, paper

❖ Stickers, glitter glue, sequins, beads,
felt tip pens or coloured pencils to
decorate your designs

What to do now

1. Trace over the templates on the page opposite as many times as you like and make a whole new wardrobe of clothes for Poppy and Honey – anything from jeans to fancy ball gowns

2. Remember to cut around the tabs as well so that you can fix your designs onto the Poppy and Honey models – just fold the tabs over the edge

3. Ask a grown-up to cut out the Poppy and Honey models below, including the base. Do not cut out the area between their legs as it will help to support the models – have fun dressing them up!

4. Cut out the stands below and stick to the backs of your Poppy and Honey models so they can stand up. Fold along the dotted line first then stick the stand down the centre of the model's legs

Poppy

Honey

THESE ARE THE STANDS
FOR YOUR MODELS